The Brave Women
Who Saved Moses

חָיוּ אֶת מֹשֶׁה

The Brave Women
Who Saved Moses

Adapted by
Alison Greengard

Illustrated by
Carol Racklin-Siegel

EXCERPTED FROM
THE BOOK OF EXODUS

EKS Publishing Co., Oakland, California

For our family who perished in the Shoah.
—Alison

For Eitan Lev Pearson.
—Carol

Adapted by Alison Greengard

Illustrated by Carol Racklin-Siegel

Edited by Jessica Goldstein and Inna Inker

Book Design by Irene Imfeld

Composition by Scott Perry

EKS Publishing Co.
P.O. Box 9750   Berkeley, CA 94709-0750
email: orders@ekspublishing.com
Phone (510) 251-9100   Fax (510) 251-9102
www.ekspublishing.com

First Printing September 2009
ISBN 978-0-939144-62-4

Introduction

The Brave Women Who Saved Moses continues the EKS Publishing series of Bible stories for young readers. Stories about Moses begin in the second chapter of Exodus and continue through the final chapter of Deuteronomy. For this installment, we have focused on the story of Moses' origins as told in Exodus 1-2.

Moses appears on the historical landscape after the patriarchs and before the kings, and it would be hard to name a more central or important figure in all of the Hebrew Bible. Indeed, Moses is traditionally held as Israel's first prophet, the man through whom the Torah was written, and a consummate teacher and leader. Moses, saved as a baby by courageous women who defy Pharaoh's evil decree to kill every newborn Jewish boy, is chosen by God to be the instrument in saving his people from slavery.

The centrality of women and emphasis on their courageous deeds makes this episode unique in the Hebrew Bible. And yet, more in keeping with tradition, only two of the women, the midwives Puah and Shifrah, are named in the text that tells of their bravery. Two other women, Moses' mother Yocheved and his sister Miriam, are named elsewhere, his mother only in genealogies that appear later in Exodus and Numbers. The Egyptian princess who takes pity on Moses and raises him as her own is never named. What's more, the text is unclear as to whether Puah and Shifrah were Hebrew mid-wives or Egyptian midwives to the Hebrews. Hebrew or Egyptian, named or nameless, the women in Exodus are at least partially responsible for the Hebrews' redemption from Egypt.

We hope that readers of all ages will enjoy this first story about Moses and come to appreciate the language and beauty of the Hebrew Bible.

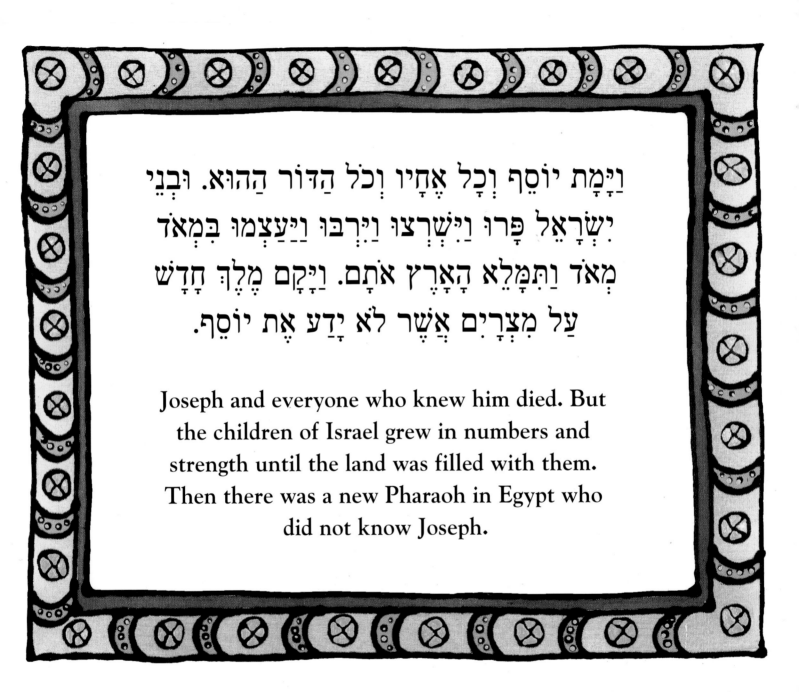

וַיָּמָת יוֹסֵף וְכָל אֶחָיו וְכֹל הַדּוֹר הַהוּא. וּבְנֵי
יִשְׂרָאֵל פָּרוּ וַיִּשְׁרְצוּ וַיִּרְבּוּ וַיַּעַצְמוּ בִּמְאֹד
מְאֹד וַתִּמָּלֵא הָאָרֶץ אֹתָם. וַיָּקָם מֶלֶךְ חָדָשׁ
עַל מִצְרָיִם אֲשֶׁר לֹא יָדַע אֶת יוֹסֵף.

Joseph and everyone who knew him died. But
the children of Israel grew in numbers and
strength until the land was filled with them.
Then there was a new Pharaoh in Egypt who
did not know Joseph.

וַיֹּאמֶר אֶל עַמּוֹ הִנֵּה עַם בְּנֵי יִשְׂרָאֵל רַב וְעָצוּם מִמֶּנּוּ, וַיַּעֲבִדוּ מִצְרַיִם אֶת בְּנֵי יִשְׂרָאֵל בְּפָרֶךְ. וַיְמָרְרוּ אֶת חַיֵּיהֶם בַּעֲבֹדָה קָשָׁה בְּחֹמֶר וּבִלְבֵנִים וּבְכָל עֲבֹדָה בַּשָּׂדֶה אֵת כָּל עֲבֹדָתָם אֲשֶׁר עָבְדוּ בָהֶם בְּפָרֶךְ.

Pharaoh said to his people, "There are too many Israelites, and they are too strong!" So the Egyptians were very hard on the Israelites. They made their lives bitter. The Israelites were forced to build with mortar and brick and to work in the fields.

וַיֹּאמֶר מֶלֶךְ מִצְרַיִם לַמְיַלְּדֹת הָעִבְרִיֹּת שֶׁפְּרָה
וְפוּעָה, וַיֹּאמֶר בְּיַלֶּדְכֶן אֶת הָעִבְרִיּוֹת וּרְאִיתֶן אִם
בֵּן הוּא וַהֲמִתֶּן. וַתִּירֶאןָ הַמְיַלְּדֹת אֶת הָאֱלֹהִים
וְלֹא עָשׂוּ כַּאֲשֶׁר דִּבֶּר אֲלֵיהֶן מֶלֶךְ מִצְרָיִם
וַתְּחַיֶּיןָ אֶת הַיְלָדִים.

Pharaoh spoke to Shifrah and Puah, the Hebrew
women who helped babies to be born. He said, "If you
see a baby boy, do not let him live!" But Shifrah and
Puah loved God and didn't do what Pharaoh had
commanded them. Instead, they saved every baby boy.

6

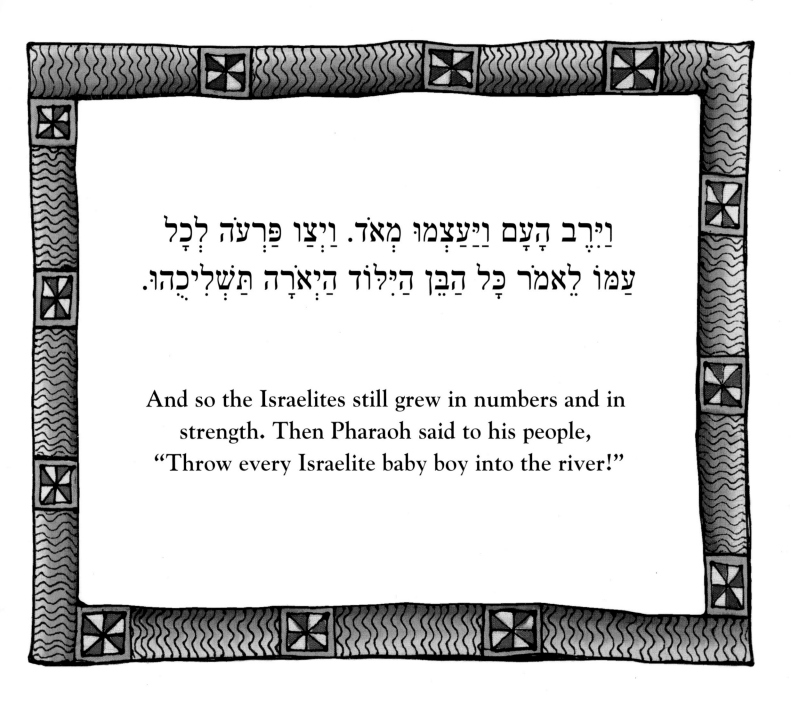

וַיִּרֶב הָעָם וַיַּעַצְמוּ מְאֹד. וַיְצַו פַּרְעֹה לְכָל
עַמּוֹ לֵאמֹר כָּל הַבֵּן הַיִּלּוֹד הַיְאֹרָה תַּשְׁלִיכֻהוּ.

And so the Israelites still grew in numbers and in
strength. Then Pharaoh said to his people,
"Throw every Israelite baby boy into the river!"

וַתַּהַר הָאִשָּׁה וַתֵּלֶד בֵּן וַתֵּרֶא אֹתוֹ כִּי טוֹב
הוּא וַתִּצְפְּנֵהוּ שְׁלֹשָׁה יְרָחִים.

During this time, an Israelite woman gave birth
to a baby boy. And when she saw how
beautiful he was, she hid him for three months.

11

וְלֹא יָכְלָה עוֹד הַצְּפִינוֹ וַתִּקַּח לוֹ תֵּבַת גֹּמֶא
וַתַּחְמְרָה בַחֵמָר וּבַזָּפֶת וַתָּשֶׂם בָּה אֶת הַיֶּלֶד
וַתָּשֶׂם בַּסּוּף עַל שְׂפַת הַיְאֹר. וַתֵּתַצַּב אֲחֹתוֹ
מֵרָחֹק לְדֵעָה מַה יֵּעָשֶׂה לוֹ.

When she couldn't hide him any longer, she put
her baby in a basket of reeds that she had sealed
with tar and set him along the banks of the river.
His sister stood watching from far away to see
what would happen to him.

וַתֵּרֶד בַּת פַּרְעֹה לִרְחֹץ עַל הַיְאֹר. וַתֵּרֶא אֶת הַתֵּבָה בְּתוֹךְ הַסּוּף וַתִּשְׁלַח אֶת אֲמָתָה וַתִּקָּחֶהָ. וַתִּפְתַּח וַתִּרְאֵהוּ אֶת הַיֶּלֶד וְהִנֵּה נַעַר בֹּכֶה וַתַּחְמֹל עָלָיו וַתֹּאמֶר מִיַּלְדֵי הָעִבְרִים זֶה.

Pharaoh's daughter went down to the river to bathe. She saw the basket in the middle of the reeds and sent her maid to bring it to her. When she opened it, she saw the baby boy, and he was crying. She felt sorry for him and said, "This must be a Hebrew child!"

וַתֹּאמֶר אֲחֹתוֹ אֶל בַּת פַּרְעֹה הַאֵלֵךְ וְקָרָאתִי לָךְ אִשָּׁה מֵינֶקֶת מִן הָעִבְרִיֹּת. וַתֹּאמֶר לָהּ בַּת פַּרְעֹה לֵכִי וַתֵּלֶךְ הָעַלְמָה וַתִּקְרָא אֶת אֵם הַיָּלֶד. וַתֹּאמֶר לָהּ בַּת פַּרְעֹה הֵילִיכִי אֶת הַיֶּלֶד הַזֶּה וַאֲנִי אֶתֵּן אֶת שְׂכָרֵךְ וַתִּקַּח הָאִשָּׁה הַיֶּלֶד וַתְּנִיקֵהוּ.

Then the baby's sister came over and said to Pharaoh's daughter, "Do you want me to find a Hebrew nurse for him?" And the princess answered, "Go!" So the young girl went and got the baby's mother, and the princess said to her, "Take care of this baby for me, and I will pay you." So the woman took the baby boy, her own son, and raised him.

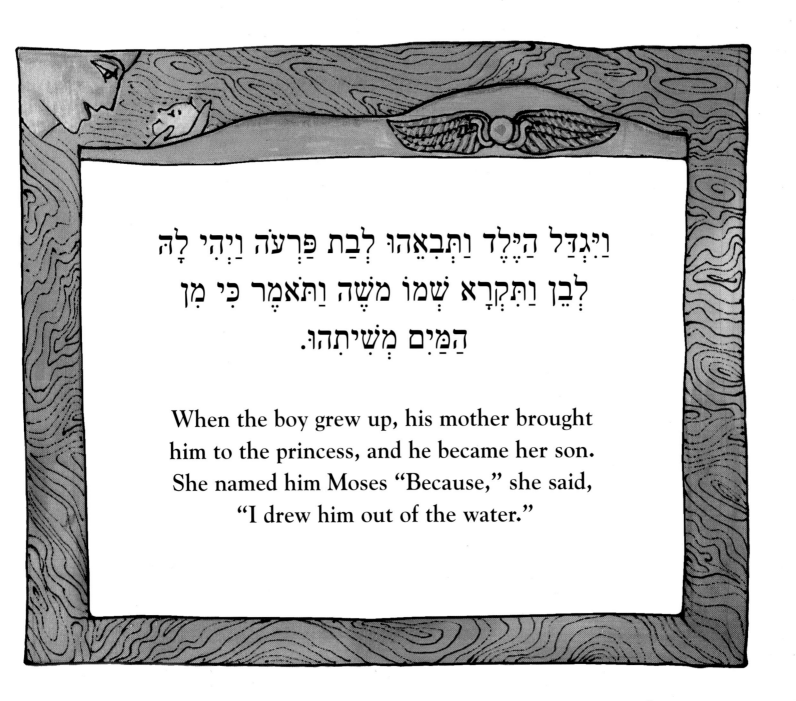

וַיִּגְדַּל הַיֶּלֶד וַתְּבִאֵהוּ לְבַת פַּרְעֹה וַיְהִי לָהּ
לְבֵן וַתִּקְרָא שְׁמוֹ מֹשֶׁה וַתֹּאמֶר כִּי מִן
הַמַּיִם מְשִׁיתִהוּ.

When the boy grew up, his mother brought
him to the princess, and he became her son.
She named him Moses "Because," she said,
"I drew him out of the water."

Literal Translation

Then Joseph died, and all of his brothers, and that whole generation. But the Israelites were fruitful and prolific; they multiplied and increased very greatly until the land was filled with them. Now a new king arose over Egypt who did not know Joseph.

He [Pharaoh] said to his people, "Look! The Israelites are too numerous and too strong for us." The Egyptians ruthlessly imposed on the Israelites and made their lives bitter with hard service with brick and mortar and with every kind of work in the field.

The king of Egypt spoke to the Hebrew midwives, Shifrah and Puah, and said, "When you deliver the Hebrew women, look at [the birthstool]. If it is a boy, kill him. But the midwives feared God and did not do what the king of Egypt had commanded them; they let the boys live. And thus the people grew numerous and very strong. Then Pharaoh commanded all his people, "Every boy that is born, you shall throw into the Nile."

The woman conceived and bore a son, and when she saw how beautiful he was, she hid him for three months. When she could hide him no longer, she got a wicker basket for him and caulked it with bitumen and pitch. She put the child in it and placed it among the reeds by the bank of the Nile. His sister stood watching him from a distance to see what would happen to him.

Pharaoh's daughter came down to the river to bathe. She saw the basket in the midst of the reeds and sent her maid to bring it to her. When she opened it she saw the child. He was crying, and she took pity on him and said, "This must be one of the Hebrews' children." Then his sister said to Pharaoh's daughter, "Shall I get you a nurse from among the Hebrew women?" And Pharaoh's daughter said to her, "Yes." So the girl went and called the child's mother. Pharaoh's daughter said to her, "Take this child, and I will pay your wages." So the woman took the child.

When the child grew up, she brought him to Pharaoh's daughter, and she took him as her son. She named him Moses, explaining, "I drew him out of the water."

א

אֶחָיו	e-**chav**	his brothers
אֲחֹתוֹ	a-cho-**to**	his sister
אֶל	**el**	to
אֲלֵיהֶן	a-lay-**hen**	to them
אִם	**eem**	if
אֵם	**aym**	mother
אֲמָתָהּ	a-ma-**ta**	her maid
אִשָּׁה	eesh-**sha**	woman
אֲשֶׁר	a-**sher**	that
אֶת/אֵת	**et/ayt**	not translatable
אֹתוֹ	o-**to**	him
אֹתָם	o-**tam**	them
אֶתֵּן	e-**tayn**	I will give

ב

בָּהּ	**bah**	in it
בָּהֶם	va-**hem**	for them
בְּחֹמֶר	be-**cho**-mer	with severity
בַּחֵמָר	va-chay-**mar**	with tar
בְּיַלֶּדְכֶן	be-yal-**led**-chen	in giving birth
בֹּכֶה	bo-**che**	was crying
בִּמְאֹד	beem-**od**	greatly

אבגדהוזחטיכלמנסעפצקרשת

21

בֵּן	**bayn**	a son
בְּנֵי	be-**nay**	children of
בַּסוּף	ba-**soof**	in the reeds
בַּעֲבֹדָה	ba-a-vo-**da**	with work
בְּפָרֶךְ	be-**fa**-rech	with oppression
בַּשָּׂדֶה	ba-sa-**de**	in the field
בַּת	**bat**	the daughter of
בְּתוֹךְ	be-**toch**	in the middle of

ג

גֹּמֶא	**go**-me	reed

ד

דִּבֶּר	deeb-**ber**	were told

ה

הָאֱלֹהִים	ha-e-lo-**heem**	the Lord
הָאֵלֵךְ	ha-ay-**laych**	I will go
הָאָרֶץ	ha-**a**-rets	the land
הָאִשָּׁה	ha-eesh-**sha**	the woman
הַבֵּן	ha-**bayn**	the son
הַדּוֹר	ha-**dor**	the generation
הַהוּא	ha-**hoo**	that
הוּא	**hoo**	he
הַזֶּה	ha-**ze**	this
הַיְאֹר	ha-ye-**or**	the river

הַיְאֹרָה	ha-ye-o-**ra**	into the river
הַיֶּלֶד/הַיָּלֶד	ha-**ye**-led/ha-**ya**-led	the boy/child/son
הַיְלָדִים	ha-ye-la-**deem**	the children
הַיִּלּוֹד	ha-yeel-**lod**	born
הֵילִיכִי	hay-**lee**-chee	take care of
הַמְיַלְּדֹת	ha-me-yal-le-**dot**	the midwives
הַמַּיִם	ha-**ma**-yeem	the water
הִנֵּה	hee-**nay**	behold
הַסּוּף	ha-**soof**	the reeds
הָעִבְרִיּוֹת, הָעִבְרִית	ha-eev-ree-**yot**	the Hebrew women
הָעִבְרִים	ha-eev-**reem**	the Hebrews
הָעַלְמָה	ha-**al**-ma	the young girl
הָעָם	ha-**am**	the people, the nation
הַצְּפִינוֹ	ha-tse-**fee**-no	to hide him
הַתֵּבָה	ha-tay-**va**	the basket

ו

וַאֲנִי	va-a-**nee**	and I
וּבַזֶּפֶת	oo-va-**za**-fet	and with tar
וּבְכָל	oo-ve-**chol**	and all
וּבִלְבֵנִים	oo-veel-vay-**neem**	and bricks
וּבְנֵי	oo-ve-**nay**	and the children of
וַהֲמִתֶּן	va-ha-mee-**ten**	you will kill them
וְהִנֵּה	ve-**hee**-nay	and behold

וַיֹּאמֶר	va-yo-mer	he said
וַיִּגְדַּל	va-yeeg-dal	he grew
וַיְהִי	vai-hee	and he was
וַיְמָרְרוּ	vai-mar-re-roo	they made bitter
וַיָּמָת	va-ya-mat	he died
וַיַּעֲבִדוּ	va-ya-a-vee-doo	they enslaved
וַיַּעַצְמוּ	va-ya-ats-moo	they grew in strength
וַיְצַו	vai-tsav	he commanded
וַיָּקָם	va-ya-kam	he arose
וַיִּרֶב	va-yee-rev	grew large
וַיִּרְבּוּ	va-yee-reb-boo	and they became many
וַיִּשְׁרְצוּ	va-yeesh-re-tsoo	they abounded
וְכֹל, וְכָל	ve-chol	and all
וְלֹא	ve-lo	and not
וְעָצוּם	ve-a-tsoom	and strong
וּפוּעָה	ve-poo-a	and Puah
וְקָרָאתִי	ve-ka-ra-tee	I will call
וּרְאִיתֶן	oo-re-ee-ten	you will see
וַתֹּאמֶר	va-to-mer	she said
וַתִּירֶאןָ	va-tee-re-na	they feared
וַתְּבִאֵהוּ	vat-vee-ay-hoo	she brought him
וַתַּהַר	va-ta-har	she became pregnant
וַתְּחַיֶּיןָ	vat-chay-ye-na	they let them live
וַתַּחְמֹל	va-tach-mol	she pitied
וַתַּחְמְרָה	va-tach-me-ra	she tarred

וַתֵּלֶד	va-**tay**-led	she gave birth to
וַתֵּלֶךְ	va-tay-**lech**	she went
וַתִּמָּלֵא	va-teem-ma-**lay**	was filled
וַתִּפְתַּח	va-teef-**tach**	she opened
וַתִּצְפְּנֵהוּ	va-teets-pe-**nay**-hoo	she hid him
וַתִּקַּח	va-teek-**kach**	she took
וַתִּקָּחֶהָ	va-teek-ka-**che**-ha	she took him
וַתִּקְרָא	va-teek-**ra**	she called
וַתֵּרֶא	va-**tay**-re	she saw
וַתִּרְאֵהוּ	va-teer-**ay**-hoo	they saw
וַתֵּרֶד	va-tay-**red**	she went down
וַתִּשְׁלַח	va-teesh-**lach**	she sent
וַתָּשֶׂם	va-ta-**sem**	she put
וַתִּתַצַּב	va-tay-tats-**tsav**	she stood

ז

זֶה	**ze**	this

ח

חָדָשׁ	cha-**dash**	new
חַיֵּיהֶם	cha-**yay**-hem	their lives

ט

טוֹב	**tov**	good, beautiful

25

יָדַע	ya-**da**	he knew
יוֹסֵף	yo-**sayf**	Joseph
יָכְלָה	ya-che-**la**	she could
יֵעָשֶׂה	yay-a-**se**	what would be done
יְרָחִים	ye-ra-**cheem**	months
יִשְׂרָאֵל	yees-ra-**ayl**	Israel

כַּאֲשֶׁר	ka-a-**sher**	that
כִּי	**kee**	because
כָּל	**kol**	all

לֹא	**lo**	did not
לֵאמֹר	lay-**mor**	as follows
לְבֵן	le-**vayn**	for a son
לְבַת	le-**vat**	to the daughter of
לָדֵעָה	le-day-**a**	to know
לָהּ	**la**	for her, to her
לוֹ	**lo**	to him
לָךְ	**lach**	to you, for you
לְכִי	lay-**chee**	go!
לְכָל	le-**chol**	to all
לַמְיַלְּדֹת	la-me-yal-le-**dot**	to the midwives

לִרְחֹץ	leer-**chots**	to bathe

מ

מְאֹד	me-**od**	very, greatly
מַה	**ma**	what
מִיַּלְדֵי	mee-yal-**day**	from the children of
מֵינֶקֶת	may-**ne**-ket	baby boy from
מֶלֶךְ	**me**-lech	king
מִמֶּנּוּ	mee-**me**-noo	from us
מִן	**meen**	from
מִצְרַיִם	meets-**ra**-yeem	Egypt
מֵרָחֹק	may-ra-**chok**	from afar
מֹשֶׁה	mo-**she**	Moses
מְשִׁיתִהוּ	me-shee-**tee**-hoo	he was drawn

נ

נַעַר	**na**-ar	a youth

ע

עֲבֹדָה	a-vo-**da**	work
עָבְדוּ	a-ve-**doo**	they worked
עֲבֹדָתָם	a-vo-da-**tam**	their work
עוֹד	**od**	any more
עַל	**al**	on, beside, along
עָלָיו	a-**lav**	for him
עַם	**am**	people, nation

עַמּוֹ	a-**mo**	his people, his nation
עָשׂוּ	a-**soo**	they did

פ

פָּרוּ	pa-**roo**	they multiplied
פַּרְעֹה	par-**o**	Pharaoh

ק

קָשָׁה	ka-**sha**	hard

ר

רַב	**rav**	many

שׁ

שְׁלֹשָׁה	she-lo-**sha**	three
שְׁמוֹ	she-**mo**	his name
שִׁפְרָה	sheef-**ra**	Shifrah

שׂ

שְׂכָרֵךְ	se-cha-**raych**	your wages
שְׂפַת	se-**fat**	on the banks of

ת

תֵּבַת	tay-**vat**	basket of
תַּשְׁלִיכֻהוּ	tash-lee-**choo**-hoo	throw them!